Small is the wren,
　　Black is the rook,
Great is the sinner
　　That steals this book.

VOICES

an anthology of poems and pictures

edited by GEOFFREY SUMMERFIELD

the third book

Rand McNally & Company · CHICAGO

Acknowledgements

For permission to reprint copyrighted material in this volume, grateful acknowledgement is made to the following:

Aldine Publishing Company: For "An Addition to the Family," "Linoleum Chocolate," "O Pioneers!" and "Spacepoem 1: from Laika to Gagarin," all reprinted from Edwin Morgan, *The Second Life* (Edinburgh: Edinburgh University Press, 1968); copyright © by Edwin Morgan and Edinburgh University Press.

Mark Allan: For "Flower: 1 Million B. C." and "Rehearsal." Reprinted by permission of the author.

John Blight and Angus and Robertson, Ltd.: For "Death of a Whale" from *A Beachcomber's Diary* by John Blight.

Jacques Chambrun, Inc.: For "Ambition" from *A Bowl of Bishop* by Morris Bishop.

Collins-Knowlton-Wing, Inc.: For "Brother" from *Collected Poems 1955* (published by Doubleday in 1955), "Traveller's Curse after Misdirection" from *Poems 1914-1926* (published by Doubleday, Doran & Co. in 1929), and "Welsh Incident" from *Collected Poems* (published by Random House in 1939), all by Robert Graves. Copyright © 1925, 1929, 1938, 1939, 1948, 1953, and 1958 by Robert Graves. Reprinted by permission of Collins-Knowlton-Wing, Inc.

Constable Publishers: For "Blaming Sons" by Ch'ien. From *170 Chinese Poems* by Arthur Waley. Reprinted by permission of Constable and Company Ltd.

Doubleday & Company, Inc.: For "The Thing" from *The Collected Poems of Theodore Roethke*. Copyright © 1963 by Beatrice Roethke as Executrix of the Estate of Theodore Roethke. Reprinted by permission of Doubleday & Company, Inc.

Dufour Editions, Inc.: For "Dead Dog" by Vernon Scannell, from *A Sense of Danger*.

Norma Millay Ellis: For "A Buck in the Snow" by Edna St. Vincent Millay, from *Collected Poems*, published by Harper & Row, Inc. Copyright 1928, 1955 by Edna St. Vincent Millay and Norma Millay Ellis. Reprinted by permission of Norma Millay Ellis.

Mari Evans: For "The Rebel" by Mari Evans. Reprinted by permission of the author.

Farrar, Straus & Giroux, Inc.: For "The Fish" and "Jeronimo's House," reprinted with the permission of Farrar, Straus & Giroux, Inc. From *Collected Poems* by Elizabeth Bishop. Copyright 1940, 1946, 1947, 1948, 1949, 1951, 1952, 1955 by Elizabeth Bishop.

(Acknowledgements continued on page 122)

Editorial Director: Joy Zweigler
Cover photographs by Dan Morrill

Contents

The Term

A rumpled sheet
of brown paper
about the length

and apparent bulk
of a man was
rolling with the

wind slowly over
and over in
the street as

a car drove down
upon it and
crushed it to

the ground. Unlike
a man it rose
again rolling

with the wind over
and over to be as
it was before.

WILLIAM CARLOS WILLIAMS

Yes It Hurts

Yes it hurts when buds burst.
Why otherwise would spring hesitate?
Why otherwise was all warmth and longing
locked under pale and bitter ice?
The blind bud covered and numb all winter,
what fever for the new compells it to burst?
Yes it hurts when buds burst,
there is pain when something grows
                and when something must close.
Yes it hurts when the ice drops melts.
Shivering, anxious, swollen it hangs,
gripping the twig but beginning to slip —
its weight tugs it downward, though it resists.
It hurts to be uncertain, cowardly, dissolving,
to feel the pull and call of the depth,
yet to hang and only shiver —
to want to remain, keep firm —
                yet want to fall.
Then, when it is worst and nothing helps,
they burst, as if in ecstasy, the first buds of the tree,
when fear itself is compelled to let go,
they fall in a glistening veil, all the drops from the twigs,
blinking away their fears of the new,
shutting out their doubts about the journey,
feeling for an instant how this is their greatest safety,
to trust in that daring
                that shapes the world.

KARIN BOYE Translated from the Swedish by May Swenson

A Boy's Head

In it there is a space-ship
and a project
for doing away with piano lessons.

And there is
Noah's ark,
which shall be first.

And there is
an entirely new bird,
an entirely new hare,
an entirely new bumble-bee.

There is a river
that flows upwards.

There is a multiplication table.

There is anti-matter.

And it just cannot be trimmed.

I believe
that only what cannot be trimmed
is a head.

There is much promise
in the circumstance
that so many people have heads.

MIROSLAV HOLUB Translated from the Czech by Ian Milner

Wanting the Impossible

Suppose he wishes balloon routes
        to five new moons, one woman,
        and a two-acre bean farm with
        bean poles and waltzing scare-
        crows wearing clown hats:
Ah-hah, ah-hah, this to God,
        this to me, this is something.

CARL SANDBURG

There Was a Man

There was a man with a tongue of wood
Who essayed to sing,
And in truth it was lamentable.
But there was one who heard
The clip-clapper of this tongue of wood
And knew what the man
Wished to sing,
And with that the singer was content.

STEPHEN CRANE

A Strange Place

A strange place
A place unknown
Only a stone's throw
From the Human race.

It is not deep
It is not wide
It is not tall.
Or small.

This place you shall never find
For it is mine and mine alone.
Strangest of all
No place is so unknown.

PETER RAKE Age 12 England

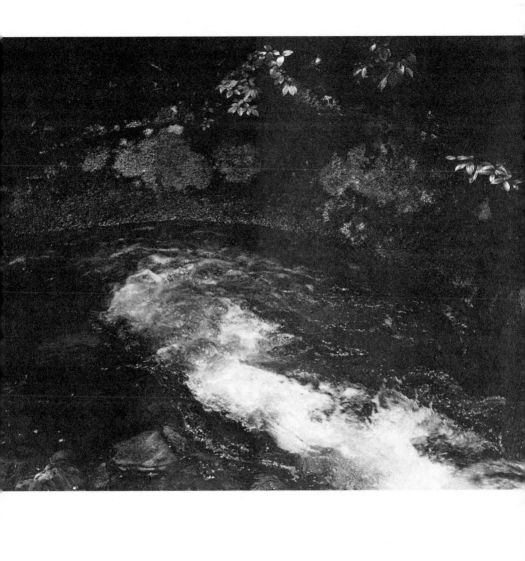

"Out, Out—"

The buzz saw snarled and rattled in the yard
And made dust and dropped stove-length sticks of wood,
Sweet-scented stuff when the breeze drew across it.
And from there those that lifted eyes could count
Five mountain ranges one behind the other
Under the sunset far into Vermont.
And the saw snarled and rattled, snarled and rattled,
As it ran light, or had to bear a load.
And nothing happened: day was all but done.
Call it a day, I wish they might have said
To please the boy by giving him the half hour
That a boy counts so much when saved from work.
His sister stood beside them in her apron
To tell them "Supper." At the word, the saw,
As if to prove saws knew what supper meant,
Leaped out at the boy's hand, or seemed to leap —
He must have given the hand. However it was,
Neither refused the meeting. But the hand!
The boy's first outcry was a rueful laugh,
As he swung toward them holding up the hand
Half in appeal, but half as if to keep
The life from spilling. Then the boy saw all —
Since he was old enough to know, big boy
Doing a man's work, though a child at heart —
He saw all spoiled. "Don't let him cut my hand off —
The doctor, when he comes. Don't let him, sister!"
So. But the hand was gone already.
The doctor put him in the dark of ether.
He lay and puffed his lips out with his breath.
And then — the watcher at his pulse took fright.
No one believed. They listened at his heart.
Little — less — nothing! — and that ended it.
No one to build on there. And they, since they
Were not the one dead, turned to their affairs.

ROBERT FROST

Those Winter Sundays

Sundays too my father got up early
and put his clothes on in the blueblack cold,
then with cracked hands that ached
from labor in the weekday weather made
banked fires blaze. No one ever thanked him.

I'd wake and hear the cold splintering, breaking.
When the rooms were warm, he'd call,
and slowly I would rise and dress,
fearing the chronic angers of that house,

Speaking indifferently to him,
who had driven out the cold
and polished my good shoes as well.
What did I know, what did I know
of love's austere and lonely offices?

ROBERT HAYDEN

Boy with His Hair Cut Short

Sunday shuts down on this twentieth-century evening.
The L passes. Twilight and bulb define
the brown room, the overstuffed plum sofa,
the boy, and the girl's thin hands above his head.
A neighbor's radio sings stocks, news, serenade.

He sits at the table, head down, the young clear neck exposed,
watching the drugstore sign from the tail of his eye;
tattoo, neon, until the eye blears, while his
solicitous tall sister, simple in blue, bending
behind him, cuts his hair with her cheap shears.

The arrow's electric red always reaches its mark,
successful neon! He coughs, impressed by that precision.
His child's forehead, forever protected by his cap,
is bleached against the lamplight as he turns head
and steadies to let the snippets drop.

Erasing the failure of weeks with level fingers,
she sleeks the fine hair, combing: "You'll look fine tomorrow!
You'll surely find something, they can't keep turning you down;
the finest gentleman's not so trim as you!" Smiling, he raises
the adolescent forehead wrinkling ironic now.

He sees his decent suit laid out, new-pressed,
his carfare on the shelf. He lets his head fall, meeting
her earnest hopeless look, seeing the sharp blades splitting,
the darkened room, the impersonal sign, her motion,
the blue vein, bright on her temple, pitifully beating.

MURIEL RUKEYSER

A Winter Scene

The noses are running at our house.
Like faucets. Wild horses.
Otherwise it is quiet here;
There is nothing afoot except Lassie who is running
Hastily through a TV pasture in quest of a
TV doctor, while we
Who are not running (except for our noses)
Vegetate (off TV) with Vicks and prescriptions
In an atmosphere so sedentary that if
We ever get well and get up and regain the potential
For running again with more than just our noses,
We may not.
          I mean it is possible
That when we get well we will not undertake to run
Or even to walk (though we'll be able to),
But will hold firm to our sofas and spread our Vicks
Ever more thickly over our throats and chests, letting Lassie
And such other TV characters as may follow
On Channel Five
Do all our running, walking, barking, thinking
For us, once even our noses
Have stopped their incessant running and it is quiet here.

REED WHITTEMORE

The Microbe

The Microbe is so very small
You cannot make him out at all,
But many sanguine people hope
To see him through a microscope.
His jointed tongue that lies beneath
A hundred curious rows of teeth;
His seven tufted tails with lots
Of lovely pink and purple spots
On each of which a pattern stands,
   Composed of forty separate bands;
     His eyebrows of a tender green;
       All these have never yet been seen —
         But scientists, who ought to know,
          Assure us that they must be so . . .
           Oh! let us never, never doubt
            What nobody is sure about!

HILAIRE BELLOC

The Air

The air was once about to die.

It cried: "O help me, Lord on high;
I am distressed and feeling sick,
am getting sluggish, getting thick;
you always know a way, Papa:
health resort send me abroad, or to a spa,
or buttermilk may cure and heal —
else to the devil I'll appeal!"

The Lord, perturbed by this affair,
invented "sound massage for air."

Since then the world is full of noise,
which thrivingly the air enjoys.

CHRISTIAN MORGENSTERN Translated from the German by Max Knight

O Pioneers!

THIS TUNNEL WAS BUGN BEGUBNUGN IN 1880 WILLIAM SHARP
Workman's inscription on entrance to abandoned Channel Tunnel at Dover

Channel Tunnel bugn.
1880. Sharp Wilgn.

Tannel Chunnel begum.
8018. Shart Willum.

Tennal Chennul gbung.
8081. Shant Willung.

Chennul Tennal bengug.
8108. Shunt Willibug.

Chunnal Tennel begbugn.
8801. Slunt Willubugmn.

Chuntenlannel begubnugn.
8810. Blunt Wuglbumlugn.

*   *   *   *   *

10880. Brigde bugn.

EDWIN MORGAN

Unintentional Paint

The flat gray banana store front
is visited by a union painter with no intentions
and a bucket of high maroon paint
and a pot of high yellow.

The high maroon banana store front
sings its contralto with two stripes
of yellow soprano on the door.

The union painter meant nothing
and we can not attribute intentions
to a bucket of maroon nor a pot of yellow.

The door and the lintels sing.
Two banjos strum on the threshold.
Two people hum a snatch of song
They know well from singing together often.
    I must come this way often
    and not only for bananas.

CARL SANDBURG

Alfred the Great

Honor and magnify this man of men
Who keeps a wife and seven children on £2 10
Paid weekly in an envelope
And yet he never has abandoned hope.

STEVIE SMITH

Money

Workers earn it,
Spendthrifts burn it,
Bankers lend it,
Women spend it,
Forgers fake it,
Taxes take it,
Dying leave it,
Heirs receive it,
Thrifty save it,
Misers crave it,
Robbers seize it,
Rich increase it,
Gamblers lose it . . .
I could use it.

RICHARD ARMOUR

Life for My Child

Life for my child is simple, and is good.
He knows his wish. Yes, but that is not all.
Because I know mine too.
And we both want joy of undeep and unabiding things,
Like kicking over a chair or throwing blocks out of a window
Or tipping over an icebox pan
Or snatching down curtains or fingering an electric outlet
Or a journey or a friend or an illegal kiss.
No. There is more to it than that.
It is that he has never been afraid.
Rather, he reaches out and lo the chair falls with a beautiful crash,
And the blocks fall, down on the people's heads,
And the water comes slooshing sloppily out across the floor.
And so forth.
Not that success, for him, is sure, infallible.
But never has he been afraid to reach.
His lesions are legion.
But reaching is his rule.

GWENDOLYN BROOKS

Fable for When There's No Way Out

Grown too big for his skin,
and it grown hard,

without a sea and atmosphere —
he's drunk it all up —

his strength's inside him now,
but there's no room to stretch.

He pecks at the top
but his beak's too soft;

though instinct and ambition shoves,
he can't get through.

Barely old enough to bleed
and already bruised!

In a case this tough
what's the use

if you break your head
instead of the lid?

Despair tempts him
to just go limp:

Maybe the cell's
already a tomb,

and beginning end
in this round room.

Still, stupidly he pecks
and pecks, as if from under

his own skull —
yet makes no crack . . .

No crack until
he finally cracks,

and kicks and stomps.
What a thrill

and shock to feel
his little gaff poke

through the floor!
A way he hadn't known or meant.

Rage works if reason won't.
When locked up, bear down.

MAY SWENSON

Gunpowder Plot

For days these curious cardboard buds have lain
In brightly colored boxes. Soon the night
Will come. We pray there'll be no sullen rain
To make these magic orchids flame less bright.

Now in the garden's darkness they begin
To flower: the frenzied whizz of Catherine-wheel
Puts forth its fiery petals and the thin
Rocket soars to burst upon the steel

Bulwark of a cloud. And then the guy,
Absurdly human phoenix, is again
Gulped by greedy flames: the harvest sky
Is flecked with threshed and glittering golden grain.

"Uncle! A cannon! Watch me as I light it!"
The women helter-skelter, squealing high,
Retreat; the paper fuse is quickly lit,
A cat-like hiss, and spit of fire, a sly

Falter, then the air is shocked with blast.
The cannon bangs and in my nostrils drifts
A bitter scent that brings the lurking past
Lurching to my side. The present shifts,

Allows a ten-year memory to walk
Unhindered now; and so I'm forced to hear
The banshee howl of mortar and the talk
Of men who died, am forced to taste my fear.

I listen for a moment to the guns,
The torn earth's grunts, recalling how I prayed.
The past retreats. I hear a corpse's sons —
"Who's scared of bangers!" "Uncle! John's afraid!"

VERNON SCANNELL

Someone

And she looked at me,
Saying with her eyes,
A lie like she always
said a lie.
And I would listen

for truths when I
listened to her,
which was rare,
but when I did,
I would try to

hear truths but,
I would never
hear them,
I would hear
only lies . . .

LEE JAFFE Age 12 U.S.A.

Not for Joseph

Joseph Baxter is my name,
    My friends all call me Joe.
I'm up, you know, to every game,
    And everything I know.
Ah, I was green as green could be,
    I suffered for it, though:
Now, if they try it on with me,
    I tell them not for Joe.
Not for Joe, not for Joe,
If he knows it, not for Joseph,
    No, no, no,
    Not for Joe,
Not for Joseph, Oh dear no!

ANONYMOUS

The Book of Lies

I'd like to have a word
with you. Could we be alone
for a minute? I have been lying
until now. Do you believe

I believe myself? Do you believe
yourself when you believe me? Lying
is natural. Forgive me. Could we be alone
forever? Forgive us all. The word

is my enemy. I have never been alone;
bribes, betrayals. I am lying
even now. Can you believe
that? I give you my word.

JAMES TATE

The Keeper of the Nore

My father he kept the Eddystone light
And he married a mer-mi-ade one night,
On account of which he had offspring three —
Two of them were fish and t'other was me.
When I was but a bit of a chip
I was put in charge of the Nore lightship:
I kept my lamps in very good style,
A-doing of the work according to Hoyle.

    Oh the rolling Nore, the raging Nore,
    The waves they tumble o'er and o'er;
    There's no such life to be had on shore,
    Like the life that is led by the man on the Nore.

lantern   One night as I was a-trimming of the glim,
A-singing a verse of the evening hymn,
I saw by the light of my signal lamp
The form of my mother looking awfully damp:
Just then a voice cries out "Ahoy!"
And there she was a-sitting on a buoy —
That's a-meaning a buoy for the ships that sail,
And not a boy that's a juvenile male.

Says I to me mother, "Now how do yer do?
And how's my father and my sisters two?"
Says she, "It's an orph-i-an you are,
For you've only one sister, and you've got no pa.
Your father was drowned with several pals
And digested by the cannibals:
Of your sisters, one was cooked in a dish,
And t'other one is kept as a talking fish."

At that I wept like a soft-eyed scamp —
My tears they made the water damp;
Says I to my mother, "Won't you step within —
You look so wet — just to dry your skin?"
Says she, "I likes the wet, my dear."
Says I, "Let me offer you the cabin chair."
My mother, she looks at me with a frown,
"It's owing to my nature that I can't sit down."

Says my mother, "Now never you go on shore,
But always remain the man at the Nore."
At that I saw a glittering scale,
And that was the end of my mother's tale.
Now, in deference to that maternal wish,
I can't visit my sister, the talking fish.
If you happen to see her when you go on shore,
Just give her the respects of the Man at the Nore.

TRADITIONAL

Liars

What kind of a liar are you?
People lie because they don't remember clear what they
    saw.
People lie because they can't help making a story better
    than it was the way it happened.
People tell "white lies" so as to be decent to others.
People lie in a pinch, hating to do it, but lying on
    because it might be worse.
And people lie just to be liars for a crooked personal
    gain.
What sort of a liar are you?
Which of these liars are you?

CARL SANDBURG

Welsh Incident

"But that was nothing to what things came out
From the sea-caves of Criccieth yonder."
"What were they? Mermaids? dragons? ghosts?"
"Nothing at all of any things like that."
"What were they, then?"
                              "All sorts of queer things,
Things never seen or heard or written about,
Very strange, un-Welsh, utterly peculiar
Things. Oh, solid enough they seemed to touch,
Had anyone dared it. Marvellous creation,
All various shapes and sizes, and no sizes,
All new, each perfectly unlike his neighbor,
Though all came moving slowly out together."
"Describe just one of them."
                              "I am unable."
"What were their colors?"
                              "Mostly nameless colors,
Colors you'd like to see; but one was puce
Or perhaps more like crimson, but not purplish.
Some had no color."
                              "Tell me, had they legs?"
"Not a leg nor foot among them that I saw."
"But did these things come out in any order?
What o'clock was it? What was the day of the week?
Who else was present? How was the weather?"
"I was coming to that. It was half-past three
On Easter Tuesday last. The sun was shining.
The Harlech Silver Band played *Marchog Jesu*
On thirty-seven shimmering instruments,
Collecting for Caernarvon's (Fever) Hospital Fund.
The populations of Pwllheli, Criccieth,
Portmadoc, Borth, Tremadoc, Penrhyndeudraeth,
Were all assembled. Criccieth's mayor addressed them
First in good Welsh and then in fluent English,
Twisting his fingers in his chain of office,
Welcoming the things. They came out on the sand,

Not keeping time to the band, moving seaward
Silently at a snail's pace. But at last
The most odd, indescribable thing of all,
Which hardly one man there could see for wonder,
Did something recognizably a something."
"Well, what?"
                    "It made a noise."
                                        "A frightening noise?"
"No, no."
            "A musical noise? A noise of scuffling?"
"No, but a very loud, respectable noise —
Like groaning to oneself on Sunday morning
In Chapel, close before the second psalm."
"What did the mayor do?"
                            "I was coming to that."

ROBERT GRAVES

The Big Nasturtiums

All of a sudden the big nasturtiums
Rose in the night from the ocean's bed,
Rested a while in the light of the morning,
Turning the sand dunes tiger red.

They covered the statue of Abraham Lincoln,
They climbed to the top of our church's spire.
"Grandpa! Grandpa! Come to the window!
Come to the window! Our world's on fire!"

Big nasturtiums in the High Sierras,
Big nasturtiums in the lands below;
Our trains are late and our planes have fallen,
And out in the ocean the whistles blow.

Over the fields and over the forests,
Over the living and over the dead —
"I never expected the big nasturtiums
To come in my lifetime!" Grandpa said.

ROBERT BEVERLY HALE

Extract from "The People, Yes"

The cauliflower is a cabbage with a college education.
All she needs for housekeeping is a can opener.
   They'll fly high if you give them wings.
Put all your eggs in one basket and watch that basket.
Everybody talks about the weather and nobody does anything
   about it.
The auk flies backward so as to see where it's been.
   Handle with care women and glass.
   Women and linen look best by candlelight.
One hair of a woman draws more than a team of horses.
Blessed are they who expect nothing for they shall not be dis-
   appointed
You can send a boy to college but you can't make him think.

The time to sell is when you have a customer.
Sell the buffalo hide after you have killed the buffalo.
The more you fill a barrel the more it weighs unless you fill it
    with holes.
A pound of iron or a pound of feathers weighs the same.
Those in fear they may cast pearls before swine are often lacking
    in pearls.
May you live to eat the hen that scratches over your grave.
He seems to think he's the frog's tonsils but he looks to me like a
    plugged nickel.
If you don't like the coat bring back the vest and I'll give you a
    pair of pants.
The coat and the pants do the work but the vest gets the gravy.
"You are singing an invitation to summer," said the teacher, "you
    are not defying it to come."

CARL SANDBURG

The Picket Fence

One time there was a picket fence
with space to gaze from hence to thence.

An architect who saw this sight
approached it suddenly one night,

removed the spaces from the fence,
and built of them a residence.

The picket fence stood there dumbfounded
with pickets wholly unsurrounded,

a view so naked and obscene,
the Senate had to intervene.

The architect, however, flew
to Afri- or Americoo.

CHRISTIAN MORGENSTERN Translated from the German by Max Knight

Boy Riding Forward Backward

Presto, pronto! Two boys, two horses.
But the boy on backward riding forward
Is the boy to watch.

He rides the forward horse and laughs
In the face of the forward boy on the backward
Horse, and *he* laughs

Back and the horses laugh. They gallop.
The trick is the cool barefaced pretense
There is no trick.

They might be flying, face to face,
On a fast train. They might be whitecaps.
Hot-cool-headed,

One curling backward, one curving forward,
Racing a rivalry of waves.
They might, they might —

Across a blue of lake, through trees,
And half a mile away I caught them:
Two boys, two horses.

Through trees and through binoculars
Sweeping for birds. Oh, they were birds
All right, all right,

Swallows that weave and wave and sweep
And skim and swoop and skitter until
The last trees take them.

ROBERT FRANCIS

Mirror

When you look
into a mirror
it is not
yourself you see,
but a kind
of apish error
posed in fearful
symmetry.

kool uoy nehW
rorrim a otni
ton si ti
,ees uoy flesruoy
dnik a tub
rorre hsipa fo
lufraef ni desop
.yrtemmys

JOHN UPDIKE

Linoleum Chocolate

Two girls running,
running laughing,
laughing lugging
two rolls of linoleum
along London Road —
a bar of chocolate
flies from the pocket
of the second, and a man
picks it up for her, she takes it
and is about to pocket it
but then unwraps it
and the girls have a bite
to recruit the strength
of their giggling progress.

EDWIN MORGAN

The Casualty

Farmers in the fields, housewives behind steamed windows,
Watch the burning aircraft across the blue sky float,
As if a firefly and a spider fought,
Far above the trees, between the washing hung out.
They wait with interest for the evening news.

But already, in a brambled ditch, suddenly-smashed
Stems twitch. In the stubble a pheasant
Is craning every way in astonishment.
The hare that hops up, quizzical, hesitant,
Flattens ears and tears madly away and the wren warns.

Some, who saw fall, smoke beckons. They jostle above,
They peer down a sunbeam as if they expected there
A snake in the gloom of the brambles or a rare flower —
See the grave of dead leaves heave suddenly, hear
It was a man fell out of the air alive,

Hear now his groans and senses groping. They rip
The slum of weeds, leaves, barbed coils; they raise
A body that as the breeze touches it glows,
Branding their hands on his bones. Now that he has
No spine, against heaped sheaves they prop him up,

Arrange his limbs in order, open his eye,
Then stand, helpless as ghosts. In a scene
Melting in the August noon, the burned man
Bulks closer greater flesh and blood than their own,
As suddenly the heart's beat shakes his body and the eye

Widens childishly. Sympathies
Fasten to the blood like flies. Here's no heart's more
Open or large than a fist clenched, and in there
Holding close complacency its most dear
Unscratchable diamond. The tears of their eyes

Too tender to let break, start to the edge
Of such horror close as mourners can,
Greedy to share all that is undergone,
Grimace, gasp, gesture of death. Till they look down
On the handkerchief at which his eye stares up.

TED HUGHES

First Blood

It was. The breech smelling of oil.
The stock of resin — buried snug
In the shoulder. Not too much recoil
At the firing of the first slug

(Jubilantly into the air)
Nor yet too little. Targets pinned
Against a tree: shot down: and there
Abandoned to the sniping wind.

My turn first to carry the gun.
Indian file and camouflaged
With contours of green shade and sun
We ghosted between larch and larch.

A movement between branches — thump
Of a fallen cone. The barrel
Jumps, making branches jump
Higher, dislodging the squirrel

To the next tree. Your turn, my turn.
The silhouette retracts its head.
A hit. "Let's go back to the lawn."
"We can't leave it carrying lead

"For the rest of its life. Reload.
Finish him off. Reload again."
It was now *him,* and when he showed
The sky cracked like a window pane.

He broke away: traversed a full
Half dozen trees: vanished. Had found
A hole? We watched that terrible
Slow spiral to the clubbing ground.

His back was to the tree. His eyes
Were gun barrels. He was dumb,
And we could not see past the size
Of his hands or hear for the drum

In his side. Four shots point-blank
To dull his eyes, a fifth to stop
The shiver in his clotted flank.
A fling of earth. As we stood up

The larches closed their ranks. And when
Earth would not muffle the drumming blood
We, like dishonored soldiers, ran
The gauntlet of a darkening wood.

JON STALLWORTHY

The Buck in the Snow

White sky, over the hemlocks bowed with snow,
Saw you not at the beginning of evening the antlered buck and
    his doe
Standing in the apple-orchard? I saw them. I saw them suddenly
    go,
Tails up, with long leaps lovely and slow,
Over the stone-wall into the wood of hemlocks bowed with snow.

Now lies he here, his wild blood scalding the snow.

How strange a thing is death, bringing to his knees, bringing to
    his antlers
The buck in the snow.
How strange a thing, — a mile away by now, it may be,
Under the heavy hemlocks that as the moments pass
Shift their loads a little, letting fall a feather of snow —
Life, looking out attentive from the eyes of the doe.

EDNA ST. VINCENT MILLAY

Ballade to a Fish of the Brooke

Why flyest thou away with fear?
Trust me, there's nought of danger near,
   I have no wicked hooke
All covered with a snaring bait,
Alas, to tempt thee to thy fate,
   And dragge thee from the brooke.

O harmless tenant of the flood,
I do not wish to spill thy blood,
   For Nature unto thee
Perchance hath given a tender wife,
And children dear, to charme thy life,
   As she hath done for me.

Enjoy thy streams, O harmless fish;
And when an angler, for his dish,
   Through gluttony's vile sin,
Attempts, a wretch, to pull thee *out,*
God give thee strength, O gentel trout,
   To pull the raskall *in!*

JOHN WOLCOT

The Physician and the Monkey

A lady sent lately for one Doctor *Drug,*
inject   To come in an Instant, and clyster poor Pug —
As the Fair one commanded he came at the Word,
And did the Grand-Office in Tie-Wig and Sword.
   The Affair being ended, so sweet and so nice,
He held out his Hand with, "You know, Ma'am, my price."
"Your Price!" says the Lady — "Why, Sir, he's a Brother,
And Doctors must never take Fees of each other."

CHRISTOPHER SMART

The Fish

I caught a tremendous fish
and held him beside the boat
half out of water, with my hook
fast in a corner of his mouth.
He didn't fight.
He hadn't fought at all.
He hung a grunting weight,
battered and venerable
and homely. Here and there
his brown skin hung in strips
like ancient wall-paper,
and its pattern of darker brown
was like wall-paper:
shapes like full-blown roses
stained and lost through age.
He was speckled with barnacles,
fine rosettes of lime,
and infested
with tiny white sea-lice,
and underneath two or three
rags of green weed hung down.
While his gills were breathing in
the terrible oxygen
— the frightening gills
fresh and crisp with blood,
that can cut so badly —
I thought of the coarse white flesh
packed in like feathers,
the big bones and the little bones,
the dramatic reds and blacks
of his shiny entrails,
and the pink swim-bladder
like a big peony.
I looked into his eyes
which were far larger than mine
but shallower, and yellowed,
the irises backed and packed
with tarnished tinfoil
seen through the lenses

mica   of old scratched isinglass.
They shifted a little, but not
to return my stare.
— It was more like the tipping
of an object toward the light.
I admired his sullen face,
the mechanism of his jaw,
and then I saw
that from his lower lip
— if you could call it a lip —
grim, wet, and weapon-like,
hung five old pieces of fish-line,
or four and a wire leader
with the swivel still attached,
with all their five big hooks
grown firmly in his mouth.
A green line, frayed at the end
where he broke it, two heavier lines,
and a fine black thread
still crimped from the strain and snap
when it broke and he got away.
Like medals with their ribbons
frayed and wavering,
a five-haired beard of wisdom
trailing from his aching jaw.
I stared and stared
and victory filled up
the little rented boat,
from the pool of bilge
where oil has spread a rainbow
around the rusted engine
to the bailer rusted orange,
the sun-cracked thwarts,
the oarlocks on their strings,
the gunnels — until everything
was rainbow, rainbow, rainbow!
And I let the fish go.

ELIZABETH BISHOP

The Ox-Tamer

In a far-away northern country in the placid pastoral region,
Lives my farmer-friend, the theme of my recitative, a famous tamer
of oxen,
There they bring him the three-year-olds and the four-year-olds to
break them,
He will take the wildest steer in the world and break him and
tame him,
He will go fearless without any whip where the young bullock
chafes up and down the yard,
The bullock's head tosses restless high in the air with raging eyes,
Yet see you! how soon his rage subsides — how soon this tamer tames
him;
See you! on the farms hereabouts a hundred oxen young and old,
and he is the man who has tamed them,
They all know him, all are affectionate to him;
See you! some are such beautiful animals, so lofty looking;
Some are buff-color'd, some mottled, one has a white line running
along his back, some are brindled.
Some have wide flaring horns (a good sign) — see you! the bright
hides,
See, the two with stars on their foreheads — see, the round bodies
and broad backs,
How straight and square they stand on their legs — what fine
sagacious eyes!
How they watch their tamer — they wish him near them — how they
turn to look after him!
What yearning expression! how uneasy they are when he moves
away from them;
Now I marvel what it can be he appears to them (books, politics,
poems, depart — all else departs),
I confess I envy only his fascination — my silent, illiterate friend,
Whom a hundred oxen love there in his life on farms,
In the northern country far, in the placid pastoral region.

WALT WHITMAN

46

Ground-Hog

Whet up yer knife and whistle up yer dogs, *(twice)*
Away to the hills to catch ground-hogs.
Ground-Hog!

They picked up their guns and went to the braish, *(twice)*
By damn, Bill, here's a hog-sign fraish.
Ground-Hog!

Hunker down, Sam, and in there peep, *(twice)*
For I think I see him sound asleep.
Ground-Hog!

Run here, Johnny, with a great long pole, *(twice)*
And roust this ground-hog outer his hole.
Ground-Hog!

Work, boys, work, as hard as you can tear, *(twice)*
This meat'll do to eat and the hide'll do to wear.
Ground-Hog!

I heard him give a whistle and a wail, *(twice)*
And I wound my stick around his tail.
Ground-Hog!

Scrape him down to his head and feet, *(twice)*
Lordy, boys, there's a fine pile o' meat.
Ground-Hog!

They put him in the pot and all began to smile, *(twice)*
They et that ground hog 'fore he struck a bile.
Ground-Hog!

The children screamed and the children cried, *(twice)*
They love ground-hog cooked and fried.
Ground-Hog!

Up stepped Sal with a snigger and a grin, *(twice)*
Ground-hog grease all over her chin.
Ground-Hog!

Run here, Mama, run here, quick, (*twice*)
I think that ground-hog's makin' me sick.
Ground-Hog!

Run here, Mama, make Bill quit, (*twice*)
He's et all the ground-hog an' I ain't had a bit.
Ground-Hog!

Ol' Aunt Sal come a-skippin' through the hall, (*twice*)
Got enough ground-hog to feed um all.
GROUND-HOG!

TRADITIONAL

Bert Kessler

I winged my bird,
Though he flew toward the setting sun;
But just as the shot rang out, he soared
Up and up through the splinters of golden light,
Till he turned right over, feathers ruffled,
With some of the down of him floating near,
And fell like a plummet into the grass.
I tramped about, parting the tangles,
Till I saw a splash of blood on a stump,
And the quail lying close to the rotten roots.
I reached my hand, but saw no brier,
But something pricked and stung and numbed it.
And then, in a second, I spied the rattler —
The shutters wide in his yellow eyes,
The head of him arched, sunk back in the rings of him,
A circle of filth, the color of ashes,
Or oak leaves bleached under layers of leaves.
I stood like a stone as he shrank and uncoiled
And started to crawl beneath the stump,
When I fell limp in the grass.

EDGAR LEE MASTERS

To the Snake

Green Snake, when I hung you round my neck
and stroked your cold, pulsing throat
      as you hissed to me, glinting
arrowy gold scales, and I felt
      the weight of you on my shoulders,
and the whispering silver of your dryness
      sounded close to my ears —

Green Snake — I swore to my companions that certainly
      you were harmless! But truly
I had no certainty, and no hope, only desiring
      to hold you, for that joy,
                which left
a long wake of pleasure, as the leaves moved
and you faded into the pattern
of grass and shadows, and I returned
smiling and haunted, to a dark morning.

DENISE LEVERTOV

Written on the Adder's Belly

If I could hear as well as see,
No man or beast should pass by me.

TRADITIONAL

Medallion

By the gate with star and moon
Worked into the peeled orange wood
The bronze snake lay in the sun

Inert as a shoelace; dead
But pliable still, his jaw
Unhinged and his grin crooked,

Tongue a rose-colored arrow.
Over my hand I hung him.
His little vermilion eye

Ignited with a glassed flame
As I turned him in the light;
When I split a rock one time

The garnet bits burned like that.
Dust dulled his back to ochre
The way sun ruins a trout.

Yet his belly kept its fire
Going under the chainmail,
The old jewels smouldering there

In each opaque belly-scale:
Sunset looked at through milk glass.
And I saw white maggots coil

Thin as pins in the dark bruise
Where his innards bulged as if
He were digesting a mouse.

Knifelike, he was chaste enough,
Pure death's-metal. The yardman's
Flung brick perfected his laugh.

SYLVIA PLATH

The Pardon

My dog lay dead five days without a grave
In the thick of summer, hid in a clump of pine
And a jungle of grass and honeysuckle-vine.
I who had loved him while he kept alive

Went only close enough to where he was
To sniff the heavy honeysuckle-smell
Twined with another odor heavier still
And hear the flies' intolerable buzz.

Well, I was ten and very much afraid.
In my kind world the dead were out of range
And I could not forgive the sad or strange
In beast or man. My father took the spade

And buried him. Last night I saw the grass
Slowly divide (it was the same scene
But now it glowed a fierce and mortal green)
And saw the dog emerging. I confess

I felt afraid again, but still he came
In the carnal sun, clothed in a hymn of flies,
And death was breeding in his lively eyes.
I started in to cry and call his name,

Asking forgiveness of his tongueless head.
. . . I dreamt the past was never past redeeming:
But whether this was false or honest dreaming
I beg death's pardon now. And mourn the dead.

RICHARD WILBUR

The Thing

Suddenly they came flying, like a long scarf of smoke,
Trailing a thing — what was it? — small as a lark
Above the blue air, in the slight haze beyond,
A thing in and out of sight,
Flashing between gold levels of the late sun,
Then throwing itself up and away from the implacable swift pursuers,
Confusing them once flying straight into the sun
So they circled aimlessly for almost a minute,
Only to find, with their long terrible eyes
The small thing diving down toward a hill,
Where they dropped again
In one streak of pursuit.

Then the first bird
Struck;
Then another, another,
Until there was nothing left,
Not even feathers from so far away.

And we turned to our picnic
Of veal soaked in marsala and little larks arranged on a long platter,
And we drank the dry harsh wine
While I poked with a stick at a stone near a four-pronged flower,
And a black bull nudged at a wall in the valley below,
And the blue air darkened.

THEODORE ROETHKE

Choose

The single clenched fist lifted and ready,
Or the open asking hand held out and waiting.
        Choose:
For we meet by one or the other.

CARL SANDBURG

Death of a Whale

When the mouse died, there was a sort of pity;
The tiny, delicate creature made for grief.
Yesterday, instead, the dead whale on the reef
Drew an excited multitude to the jetty.
How must a whale die to wring a tear?
Lugubrious death of a whale; the big
Feast for the gulls and sharks; the tug
Of the tide simulating life still there,
Until the air, polluted, swings this way
Like a door ajar from a slaughterhouse.
Pooh! pooh! spare us, give us the death of a mouse
By its tiny hole; not this in our lovely bay.
— Sorry, we are, too, when a child dies:
sacrifice   But at the immolation of a race, who cries?

JOHN BLIGHT

Flower: 1 Million B.C.

"Come up!"
Cried the Voice
With a breathy tone
And I pushed and strained
And lifted my ignorant innocent
Eyes upon the crusty earth and
Frowned even in my unknowingness
That man was still
Sleeping.

MARK ALLAN

Mushrooms

Overnight, very
Whitely, discreetly,
Very quietly

Our toes, our noses
Take hold on the loam,
Acquire the air.

Nobody sees us,
Stops us, betrays us;
The small grains make room.

Soft fists insist on
Heaving the needles,
The leafy bedding,

Even the paving.
Our hammers, our rams,
Earless and eyeless,

Perfectly voiceless,
Widen the crannies,
Shoulder through holes. We

Diet on water,
On crumbs of shadow,
Bland-mannered, asking

Little or nothing.
So many of us!
So many of us!

We are shelves, we are
Tables, we are meek,
We are edible,

Nudgers and shovers
In spite of ourselves.
Our kind multiplies:

We shall by morning
Inherit the earth.
Our foot's in the door.

SYLVIA PLATH

Original Sin

The man-brained and man-handed ground-ape, physically
The most repulsive of all hot-blooded animals
Up to that time of the world: they had dug a pitfall
And caught a mammoth, but how could their sticks and stones
Reach the life in that hide? They danced around the pit,
     shrieking
With ape excitement, flinging sharp flints in vain, and the
     stench of their bodies
Stained the white air of dawn; but presently one of them
Remembered the yellow dancer, wood-eating fire
That guards the cave-mouth: he ran and fetched him, and
    others
Gathered sticks at the wood's edge; they made a blaze
And pushed it into the pit, and they fed it high, around the
     mired sides
Of their huge prey. They watched the long hairy trunk
Waver over the stifle-trumpeting pain,
And they were happy.

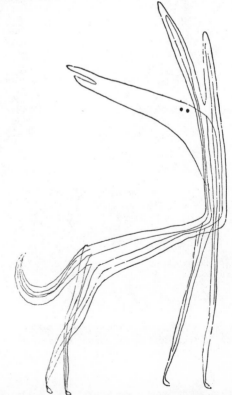

                    Meanwhile the intense color and
            nobility of sunrise.
Rose and gold and amber, flowed up the sky. Wet rocks were
        shining, a little wind
Stirred the leaves of the forest and the marsh flag-flowers;
        the soft valley between the low hills
Became as beautiful as the sky; while in its midst, hour
        after hour, the happy hunters
Roasted their living meat slowly to death.
                                These are the
        people.
This is the human dawn. As for me, I would rather
Be a worm in a wild apple than a son of man.
But we are what we are, and we might remember
Not to hate any person, for all are vicious;
And not be astonished at any evil, all are deserved;
And not fear death; it is the only way to be cleansed.

ROBINSON JEFFERS

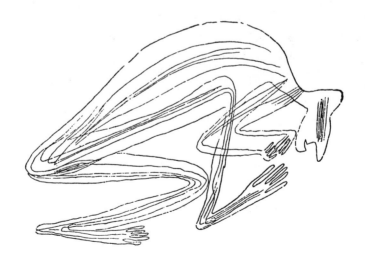

Rehearsal

Today
I had rehearsal
To stage the world's beginning.
The two main characters rehearsed
                              and
                                 rehearsed
Their lines.
And out of all that effort they forgot,
And the play went bad.

MARK ALLAN

Implications

When the charge of election bribery was brought against an Illinois senator, he replied, "I read the Bible and believe it from cover to cover."

When his accusers specified five hundred dollars of corruption money was paid in a St. Louis hotel bathroom, his friends answered, "He is faithful to his wife and always kind to his children."

When he was ousted from the national senate and the doors of his bank were closed by government receivers and a grand jury indicted him, he took the vows of an old established church.

When a jury acquitted him of guilt as a bank wrecker, following the testimony of prominent citizens that he was an honest man, he issued a statement to the public for the newspapers, proclaiming he knew beforehand no jury would darken the future of an honest man with an unjust verdict.

CARL SANDBURG

Prophecy

belief in the
improbable

When suffering is everywhere, that is of the nature of belief.
When the leaders are corrupted, Pope or Commissar,
nor do the people flicker an eyelash, that is of the
nature of belief. When there are anniversaries of battle
or martyrdom, that is of the nature of belief. When
there is the slogan *Credo quia absurdum* or intellectual
proof of the existence of God, that is of the nature of
belief. When priests pray for victory and generals
invoke heaven, when prisons fill with children, that is
of the nature of belief. When the word *evil* appears in
newspapers, *moral* in the mouths of policemen, *culture*
in the prepared speeches of politicians, all that is of the
nature of belief. Belief makes blood flow. Belief infects
the dead with more belief. Now it flows in our veins.
Now it floats in the clouds.

KARL SHAPIRO

Reading Newspapers

Sometimes Korf meets worried friends who've read
news on international relations. He advises:
Read the paper of a day ahead!

When the diplomats start fighting in the spring
just pick up an autumn paper and
see there how they settled everything.

Mostly this is done the other way around
(else, where would it leave the present day?)
But this merely means we're habit-bound.

CHRISTIAN MORGENSTERN Translated from the German by Max Knight

The Station

I am . . .
Down by the station, the old railroad station,
Where the floors are colored with ground-in dust;
The benches moan with tired, brief creaks,
Their metal legs eaten by rust.

Outside . . .
The dirt-brown stairs bake in the sun;
The paint on the walls is peeling.
Four rows of track gleam . . . and smell
Metallic and fresh — yet worn.

And . . .
You can see the heat as it patterns the air,
The blue of the sky softly rests on the roof.
All this to see, and no one to see it;
There's no one — no one but me.

Wondering . . .
The cars without the drivers,
The benches without their occupants,
Wondering at the empty loneliness of the place,
Which somehow might be filled.

JOHN RATHE Age 12 U.S.A.

Wires

The widest prairies have electric fences,
For though old cattle know they must not stray,
Young steers are always scenting purer water
Not here but anywhere. Beyond the wires

Leads them to blunder up against the wires
Whose muscle-shredding violence gives no quarter.
Young steers become old cattle from that day,
Electric limits to their wildest senses.

PHILIP LARKIN

Southbound on the Freeway

A tourist came in from Orbitville,
parked in the air, and said:

The creatures of this star
are made of metal and glass.

Through the transparent parts
you can see their guts.

Their feet are round and roll
on diagrams — or long

measuring tapes — dark
with white lines.

They have four eyes.
The two in the back are red.

Sometimes you can see a 5-eyed
one, with a red eye turning

on the top of his head.
He must be special —

the others respect him,
and go slow,

when he passes, winding
among them from behind.

They all hiss as they glide,
like inches, down the marked

tapes. Those soft shapes,
shadowy inside

the hard bodies — are they
their guts or their brains?

MAY SWENSON

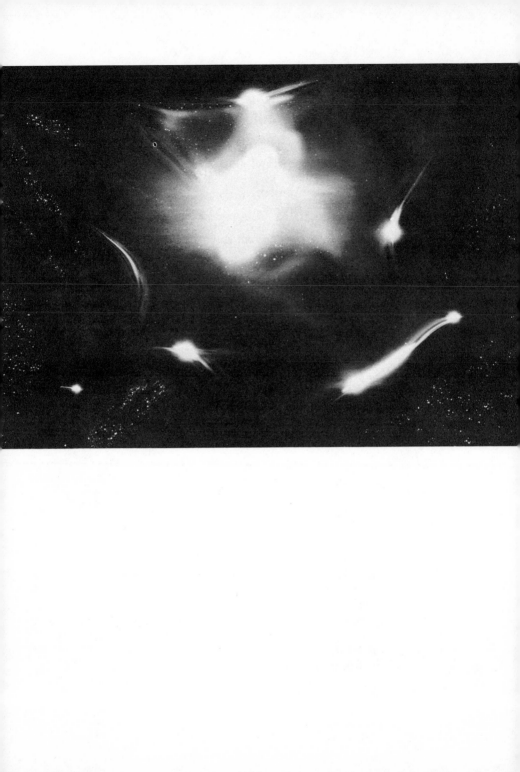

Mother Goose
(*Circa* 2054)

Humpty Dumpty sat on the wall,
A non-electro-magnetic ball.
All the Super's polariscopes
Couldn't revitalize his isotopes.

IRENE SEKULA

A.D. 2267

Once on the gritty moon (burnt earth hung far
In the black, rhinestone sky — lopsided star),
Two gadgets, with great fishbowls for a head,
Feet clubbed, hips loaded, shoulders bent. She said,
"Fantasies haunt me. A green garden. Two
Lovers aglow in flesh. The pools so blue!"
He whirrs with masculine pity, "Can't forget
Old superstitions? The earth-legend yet?"

JOHN FREDERICK NIMS

Space Poem 1 : from Laika to Gagarin

ra ke ta ra ke ta ra ke ta ra ke ta ra ke ta ra ke ta ra ke ta
sputsputsputsputsputsputsputsputsputsputsputsputsputsputsput
nik lai nik bel nik strel nik pchel nik mush nik chernush nik zvezdoch
kakakakakakakakakakakakakakakakakakakakakakakakakakakakakakakak
spu spu tink spu kak spink spu sobak spu ka kink tak so
nikka laika kalai kanikka kanaka kana sput
nikka belka kabel kanikka kanaka kana stup
nikka strelka kastrel kanikka kanaka kana pust
nikka pchelka kapchel kanikka kanaka kana psut
nikka mushka kamush kanikka kanaka kana tusp
nikka chernushka kachernush kanikka kanaka kana tsup
nikka zvezdochka kazvezdoch kanikka kanaka kana upst
barker whitiearrow beespot blackie star
whitie arrowbarker beeblackie star spot
arrow barkerbee whitiestar blackie spot
bee arrowwhitie barkerspot star blackie
barkbark! whitewhitewhite! blackblackblackblack!
star! spot! sput! stop! star! sputsput! star! spout! spurt! start!
starrow! starrow! starrow!

putputputputputputputputputputputputputputputput
nikniknikniknikniknikniknikniknikniknikniknikniknik
ka kra keta ka kra keta ka kra keta ka kra keta ka kra keta
kaktok kaktok kaktok kaktok kaktok kaktok kaktok kaktok
dakakvos dakakvos dakakvos dakakvos dakakvos dakakvos
davostok davostok davostok davostok davostok davostok
dadadadadadadadadadadadadadadadadadadadadadadadadadada
daga daga daga daga daga daga daga daga daga daga daga
dagaga dagaga dagaga dagaga dagaga dagaga dagaga dagaga
dakakgaga rin dakakgaga rin dakakgaga rin dakakgaga rin
vostok! mir! vladi! yuri! mir! vladi! vladimir! vladivostok!
yurimirny! vladimirny! yurilaika! nikitaraketa! balalaika!
raketasobakaslava! vladislava!

EDWIN MORGAN

Ambition

I got pocketed behind 7X-3824;
He was making 65, but I can do a little more.
I crowded him on the curves, but I couldn't get past,
And on the straightways there was always some truck coming fast.
Then we got to the top of a mile-long incline
And I edged her out to the left, a little over the white line,
And ahead was a long grade with construction at the bottom,
And I said to the wife, "Now by golly I got'm!"
I bet I did 85 going down the long grade,
And I braked her down hard in front of the barricade,
And I swung in ahead of him and landed fine
Behind 9W-7679.

MORRIS BISHOP

I Took My Power in My Hand

I took my Power in my Hand —
And went against the World —
'Twas not so much as David — had —
But I — was twice as bold —

I aimed my Pebble — but Myself
Was all the one that fell —
Was it Goliath — was too large —
Or was myself — too small?

EMILY DICKINSON

Dead Dog

One day I found a lost dog in the street.
The hairs about its grin were spiked with blood,
And it lay still as stone. It must have been
A little dog, for though I only stood
Nine inches for each one of my four years
I picked it up and took it home. My Mother
Squealed, and later father spaded out
A bed and tucked my mongrel down in mud.

I can't remember any feeling but
tearful A moderate pity, cool not lachrymose;
Almost a godlike feeling now it seems.
My lump of dog was ordinary as bread.
I have no recollection of the school
Where I was taught my terror of the dead.

VERNON SCANNELL

The Fox

When I saw the fox, it was kneeling
in snow: there was nothing to confess
that, tipped on its broken forepaws,
the thing was dead — save for its stillness.

A drift, confronting me, leaned down
across the hill-top field. The wind
cut it into a slope   had scarped it into a pennine wholly of snow, and
where did the hill go now?

There was no way round:
I drew booted legs
back out of it, took to my tracks again,
specks   but already a million blown snow-motes were
    flowing and filling them in.

Domed at the summit, then tapering,
the drift still mocked
my mind as if the whole
fox-infested hill were the skull of a fox.

Scallops and dips
of pure pile rippled and shone, but what
should I do with such beauty
eyed by that?

It was like clambering between its white temples
as the crosswind tore
at one's knees, and each
missed step was a plunge at the hill's blinding interior.

CHARLES TOMLINSON

Bags of Meat

"Here's a fine bag of meat,"
Says the master-auctioneer,
As the timid, quivering steer,
Starting a couple of feet
At the prod of a drover's stick,
And trotting lightly and quick,
A ticket stuck on his rump,
Enters with a bewildered jump.

"Where he's lived lately, friends,
I'd live till lifetime ends:
They've a whole life everyday
Down there in the Vale, have they!
He'd be worth the money to kill
And give away Christmas for good-will."

"Now here's a heifer — worth more
Than bid, were she bone-poor;
Yet she's round as a barrel of beer;"
"She's a plum," said the second auctioneer.

"Now this young bull — for thirty pound?
Worth that to manure your ground!"
"Or to stand," chimed the second one,
"And have his picter done!"

The beast was rapped on the horns and snout
To make him turn about.
"Well," cried a buyer, "another crown —
Since I've dragged here from Taunton Town!"
"That calf, she sucked three cows,
drink   which is not matched for bouse
In the nurseries of high life
By the first-born of a nobleman's wife!"
The stick falls, meaning, "A true tale's told,"
On the buttock of the creature sold,
And the buyer leans over and snips
His mark on one of the animal's hips.

Each beast, when driven in,
Looks round at the ring of bidders there
With a much-amazed reproachful stare,
    As at unnatural kin,
For bringing him to a sinister scene
So strange, unhomelike, hungry, mean;
His fate the while suspended between
    A butcher, to kill out of hand,
    And a farmer, to keep on the land;
One can fancy a tear runs down his face
When the butcher wins, and he's driven from the place.

THOMAS HARDY

Travelling Through the Dark

Travelling through the dark I found a deer
dead on the edge of the Wilson River road.
It is usually best to roll them into the canyon:
that road is narrow; to swerve might make more dead.

By glow of the tail-light I stumbled back of the car
and stood by the heap, a doe, a recent killing;
she had stiffened already, almost cold.
I dragged her off; she was large in the belly.

My fingers touching her side brought me the reason —
her side was warm; her fawn lay there waiting,
alive, still, never to be born.
Beside that mountain road I hesitated.

The car aimed ahead its lowered parking lights;
under the hood purred the steady engine.
I stood in the glare of the warm exhaust turning red;
around our group I could hear the wilderness listen.

I thought hard for us all — my only swerving —
then pushed her over the edge into the river.

WILLIAM STAFFORD

The Shell

And then I pressed the shell
Close to my ear,
And listened well.

And straightway, like a bell,
Came low and clear
The slow, sad murmur of far distant seas,

Whipped by an icy breeze
Upon a shore
Windswept and desolate.

It was a sunless strand that never bore
The footprint of a man,
Nor felt the weight

Since time began
Of any human quality or stir,
Save what the dreary winds and waves incur.

II

And in the hush of waters was the sound
Of pebbles, rolling round;
Forever rolling, with a hollow sound:

And bubbling seaweeds, as the waters go,
Swish to and fro
Their long cold tentacles of slimy grey;

There was no day;
Nor ever came a night
Setting the stars alight

To wonder at the moon:
Was twilight only, and the frightened croon,
Smitten to whimpers, of the dreary wind

And waves that journeyed blind . . .
And then I loosed my ear. — Oh, it was sweet
To hear a cart go jolting down the street!

JAMES STEPHENS

Girl, Boy, Flower, Bicycle

This girl
Waits at the corner for
This boy
Freewheeling on his bicycle.
She holds
A flower in her hand
A gold flower
In her hands she holds
The sun.
With power between his thighs
The boy
Comes smiling to her
He rides
A bicycle that glitters like
The wind.
This boy this girl
They walk
In step with the wind
Arm in arm
They climb the level street
To where
Laid on the glittering handlebars
The flower
Is round and shining as
The sun.

M. K. JOSEPH

Song

until I hid my love when young while I
Couldn't bear the buzzing of a flye
I hid my love to my despite
Till I could not bear to look at light
I dare not gaze upon her face
But left her memory in each place
Where ere I saw a wild flower lye
I kissed and bade my love good bye

I met her in the greenest dells
Where dew drops pearl the wood blue bells
The lost breeze kissed her bright blue eye
The bee kissed and went stinging bye
A sun beam found a passage there
A gold chain round her neck so fair
As secret as the wild bees song
She lay there all the summer long

I hid my love in field and town
Till e'en the breeze would knock me down
The Bees seemed singing ballads o'er
The flyes buss turned a Lion's roar
And èven silence found a tongue
To haunt me all the summer long
The riddle nature could not prove
Was nothing else but secret love

JOHN CLARE

Useless Words

So long as we speak the same language and never understand
        each other,
So long as the spirals of our words snarl and interlock
And clutch each other with the irreckonable gutturals,
Well . . .

CARL SANDBURG

First Ice

A girl in a phone box is freezing cold,
Retreating into her shivery coat.
Her face in too much make-up's smothered
With grubby tearstains and lipstick smudges.

Into her tender palms she's breathing.
Fingers — ice lumps. In earlobes — earrings.

She goes back home, alone, alone,
Behind her the frozen telephone.

First ice. The very first time.
First ice of a telephone conversation.

On her cheeks tear traces shine —
First ice of human humiliation.

ANDREI VOZNESENSKY Translated from the Russian by Herbert Marshall

The Quarrel

I quarreled with my brother,
I don't know what about,
One thing led to another
And somehow we fell out.
The start of it was slight,
The end of it was strong,
He said he was right,
I knew he was wrong!

We hated one another.
The afternoon turned black.
Then suddenly my brother
Thumped me on the back,
And said, "Oh, come along!
We can't go on all night —
I was in the wrong."
So he was in the right.

ELEANOR FARJEON

Beyond Words

That row of icicles along the gutter
Feels like my armory of hate;
And you, you . . . you, you utter . . .
You wait.

ROBERT FROST

An Answer to the Parson

"Why of the sheep do you not learn peace?"
"Because I don't want you to shear my fleece."

WILLIAM BLAKE

Big Bessie Throws Her Son into the Street

A day of sunny face and temper.
The winter trees
Are musical.

Bright lameness from my beautiful disease,
You have your destiny to chip and eat.

Be precise.
With something better than candles in the eyes.
(Candles are not enough.)

At the root of the will, a wild inflammable stuff.

New pioneer of days and ways, be gone.
Hunt out your own or make your own alone.

Go down the street.

GWENDOLYN BROOKS

Heredity

I am the family face;
Flesh perishes, I live on,
Projecting trait and trace
Through time to times anon,
And leaping from place to place
Over oblivion.

The years-heired feature that can
In curve and voice and eye
Despise the human span
Of durance — that is I;
The eternal thing in man,
That heeds no call to die.

THOMAS HARDY

Our Father

She said my father had whiskers and looked like God;
that he swore like a fettler, drank like a bottle;
used to run away from mother, left money for food;
called us by numbers; had a belt with a buckle.

On Sunday was churchday. We children walked behind.
He'd wear a stiff collar. He'd say good-morning.
And we made jokes about him, we were afraid
because already we understood about hating.

When we'd left the church that was so nice and still,
the minister would let us give the bells a telling —
four dong-dells; and we'd decide that Nell's
was to be the end of the world; it was time for going.

When we got home he'd take off his collar, and his shoes;
and his Sunday-special braces; and we'd whisper,
he's not like God. So that he'd belt us for the noise,
and we'd yell. And on Mondays he'd run away from mother.

RAY MATHEW

Blaming Sons

An Apology for His Own Drunkenness, A.D. 406

White hairs cover my temples,
I am wrinkled and gnarled beyond repair,
And though I have got five sons,
They all hate paper and brush.
A-shu is eighteen:
For laziness there is none like him.
A-hsüan does his best,
But really loathes the Fine Arts.
Yung and Tuan are thirteen,
But do not know "six" from "seven."
T'ung-tzu in his ninth year
Is only concerned with things to eat.
If Heaven treats me like this,
What can I do but fill my cup?

T'AO CH'IEN Translated from the Chinese by Arthur Waley

A Right Carry-On

When I was a chicken as big as a hen,
My mother hit me, and I hit her again;
My father came in, and said what're yer 'bout?
So I up with my fist, and I gin him a clout.

TRADITIONAL

Parents and Children

As tall as your knee, they are pretty to see;
As tall as your head, they wish you were dead.

TRADITIONAL

An Addition to the Family: for M. L.

A musical poet, collector of basset-horns,
was buttering his toast down in Dunbartonshire
when suddenly from behind the breakfast newspaper
the shining blade stopped scraping
and he cried to his wife, "Joyce, listen to this! —
'Two basset-hounds for sale, house-trained, keen hunters' —
Oh we must have them! What d'you think?" "But dear,
did you say *hounds*?" "Yes, yes, hounds, hounds — "
"But Maurice, it's *horns* we want, you must be over
in the livestock column, what would we do
with a basset-hound, you can't play a hound!"
"It's Beverley it says, the kennels are at Beverley — "
"But Maurice — " "I'll get some petrol, we'll be there by lunchtime — "
"But a dog, two dogs, where'll we put them?"
"I've often wondered what these dogs are like — "
"You mean you don't even — " "Is there no more marmalade?"
" — don't know what they look like? And how are we to feed them?
Yes, there's the pot dear." "This stuff's all peel, isn't it?"
"Well, we're at the end of it. But look, these two great — "
"You used to make marmalade once upon a time."
"They've got ears down to here, and they're far too — "
"Is that half past eight? I'll get the car out.
See if I left my checkbook on the — " "Maurice,
are you mad? What about your horns?" "What horns,
what are you talking about? Look Joyce dear,
if it's not on the dresser it's in my other jacket.
I believe they're wonderful for rabbits — "
So the musical poet took his car to Beverley
with his wife and his checkbook, and came back home
with his wife and his checkbook and two new hostages
to the unexpectedness of fortune.

The creatures scampered through the grass, the children
came out with cries of joy, there seemed to be nothing
dead or dying in all that landscape.
Fortune bless the unexpected cries!
Life gathers to the point of wishing it,
a mocking pearl of many ventures. The house
rolled on its back and kicked its legs in the air.
And later, wondering farmers as they passed would hear
behind the lighted window in the autumn evening
two handsome mellow-bosomed basset-hounds
howling to a melodious basset-horn.

EDWIN MORGAN

nobody loses all the time

nobody loses all the time

i had an uncle named
Sol who was a born failure and
nearly everybody said he should have gone
into vaudeville perhaps because my Uncle Sol could
sing McCann He Was A Diver on Xmas Eve like Hell Itself which
may or may not account for the fact that my Uncle

Sol indulged in that possibly most inexcusable
of all to use a highfalootin phrase
luxuries that is or to
wit farming and be
it needlessly
added

my Uncle Sol's farm
failed because the chickens
ate the vegetables so
my Uncle Sol had a
chicken farm till the
skunks ate the chickens when

my Uncle Sol
had a skunk farm but
the skunks caught cold and
died and so

my Uncle Sol imitated the
skunks in a subtle manner

or by drowning himself in the watertank
but somebody who'd given my Uncle Sol a Victor
Victrola and records while he lived presented to
him upon the auspicious occasion of his decease a
scrumptious not to mention splendiferous funeral with
tall boys in black gloves and flowers and everything and

i remember we all cried like the Missouri
when my Uncle Sol's coffin lurched because
somebody pressed a button
(and down went
my Uncle
Sol

and started a worm farm)

E. E. CUMMINGS

Ages of Man

1 As foolish as monkeys till twenty or more;
As bold as lions till forty and four;
As cunning as foxes till three score and ten;
Then they become asses or something — not men.

2 At ten a child; at twenty wild;
At thirty tame if ever;
At forty wise, at fifty rich;
At sixty good, or never.

TRADITIONAL

Brother

It's odd enough to be alive with others,
But odder still to have sisters and brothers:
To make one of a characteristic litter —
The sisters puzzled and vexed, the brothers vexed and bitter
That this one wears, though flattened by abuse,
The family nose for individual use.

ROBERT GRAVES

Phizzog

This face you got,
This here phizzog you carry round,
You never picked it out for yourself, at all, at all — did you?
This here phizzog — somebody handed it to you — am I right?
Somebody said, "Here's yours, now go see what you can do
      with it."
Somebody slipped it to you and it was like a package marked:
"No goods exchanged after being taken away" —
This face you got.

CARL SANDBURG

Timothy Winters

Timothy Winters comes to school
With eyes as wide as a football-pool,
Ears like bombs and teeth like splinters:
A blitz of a boy is Timothy Winters.

His belly is white, his neck is dark,
And his hair is an exclamation-mark.
His clothes are enough to scare a crow
And through his britches the blue winds blow.

When teacher talks he won't hear a word
And he shoots down dead the arithmetic-bird,
He licks the patterns off his plate
And he's not even heard of the Welfare State.

Timothy Winters has bloody feet
And he lives in a house on Suez Street,
He sleeps in a sack on the kitchen floor
And they say there aren't boys like him any more.

Old Man Winters likes his beer
And his missus ran off with a bombardier,
Grandma sits in the grate with a gin
And Timothy's dosed with an aspirin.

The Welfare Worker lies awake
But the law's as tricky as a ten-foot snake,
So Timothy Winters drinks his cup
And slowly goes on growing up.

prays At Morning Prayers the Master helves
for children less fortunate than ourselves,
And the loudest response in the room is when
Timothy Winters roars "Amen!"
So come one angel, come on ten:

Timothy Winters says "Amen
Amen amen amen amen."
Timothy Winters, Lord.
                    Amen.

CHARLES CAUSLEY

Fragment

as for him who
finds fault
may silliness

and sorrow
overtake him
when you wrote

you did not
know
the power of

your words.

WILLIAM CARLOS WILLIAMS

A Poison Tree

I was angry with my friend:
I told my wrath, my wrath did end.
I was angry with my foe:
I told it not, my wrath did grow.

And I water'd it in fears,
Night and morning with my tears;
And I sunnèd it with smiles,
And with soft deceitful wiles.

And it grew both day and night,
Till it bore an apple bright;
And my foe beheld it shine,
And he knew that it was mine,

And into my garden stole
When the night had veil'd the pole:
In the morning glad I see
My foe outstretch'd beneath the tree.

WILLIAM BLAKE

Traveller's Curse after Misdirection

(From the Welsh)

May they stumble, stage by stage
On an endless pilgrimage,
Dawn and dusk, mile after mile,
At each and every step, a stile;
At each and every step withal
May they catch their feet and fall;
At each and every fall they take
May a bone within them break;
And may the bone that breaks within
Not be, for variation's sake,
Now rib, now thigh, now arm, now shin,
But always, without fail, THE NECK.

ROBERT GRAVES

The Rebel

When I
die
I'm sure
I will have a
Big Funeral . . .
Curiosity
seekers . . .
coming to see
if I
am really
Dead . . .
or just
trying to make
Trouble . . . .

MARI EVANS

Scarborough Fair

Are you going to Scarborough Fair?
Parsley, Sage, Rosemary and Thyme.
Remember me to one who lived there,
For once she was a true love of mine.

Tell her to make me a cambric shirt —
Parsley, Sage, Rosemary and Thyme —
Without any seam or needlework.
She shall be a true love of mine.

Tell her to wash it in yonder dry well —
Parsley, Sage, Rosemary and Thyme —
Where water ne'er sprung nor drop of rain fell.
She shall be a true love of mine.

Tell her to dry it on yonder thorn —
Parsley, Sage, Rosemary and Thyme —
Where blossom ne'er grew since Adam was born.
She shall be a true love of mine.

Well, will you find me an acre of land —
Parsley, Sage, Rosemary and Thyme —
Between the sea foam and the sea sand?
You shall be a true love of mine.

And will you plough it with a lamb's horn —
Parsley, Sage, Rosemary and Thyme —
And sow it all over with one peppercorn?
And you shall be a true love of mine.

Will you reap it with a sickle of leather —
Parsley, Sage, Rosemary and Thyme —
And tie it all up with a peacock's feather?
And you shall be a true love of mine.

And when you've done and you've finished your work —
Parsley, Sage, Rosemary and Thyme —
Then come to me for your cambric shirt,
And you shall be a true love of mine.

TRADITIONAL

The Ballad of Charlotte Dymond

Charlotte Dymond, a domestic servant aged eighteen, was
murdered near Rowtor Ford on Bodmin Moor on Sunday, 14 April 1844, by her young man, a crippled farm-
hand, Matthew Weeks, aged twenty-two. A stone marks
the spot.

It was a Sunday morning
  And in the April rain
That Charlotte went from our house
  And never came home again.

Her shawl of diamond redcloth,
  She wore a yellow gown,
She carried the green gauze handkerchief
  She bought in Bodmin town.

About her throat her necklace
  And in her purse her pay:
The four silver shillings
  She had at Lady Day.

In her purse four shillings
  And in her purse her pride
As she walked out one evening
  Her lover at her side.

Out beyond the marshes
  Where the cattle stand,
With her crippled lover
  Limping at her hand.

Charlotte walked with Matthew
  Through the Sunday mist,
Never saw the razor
  Waiting at his wrist.

Charlotte she was gentle
  But they found her in the flood
Her Sunday beads among the reeds
  Beaming with her blood.

Matthew, where is Charlotte,
  And wherefore has she flown?
For you walked out together
  And now are come alone.

Why do you not answer,
  Stand silent as a tree,
Your Sunday worsted stockings
  All muddied to the knee?

Why do you mend your breast-pleat
  With a rusty needle's thread
And fall with fears and silent tears
  Upon your single bed?

Why do you sit so sadly
  Your face the color of clay
And with a green gauze handkerchief
  Wipe the sour sweat away?

Has she gone to Blisland
  To seek an easier place,
And is that why your eye won't dry
  And blinds your bleaching face?

"Take me home!" cried Charlotte,
  "I lie here in the pit!
A red rock rests upon my breasts
  and my naked neck is split!"

Her skin was soft as sable,
  Her eyes were wide as day,
Her hair was blacker than the bog
  That licked her life away.

Her cheeks were made of honey,
  Her throat was made of flame
Where all around the razor
  Had written its red name.

As Matthew turned at Plymouth
  About the tilting Hoe,
The cold and cunning Constable
  Up to him did go:

"I've come to take you, Matthew,
　　Unto the Magistrate's door.
　Come quiet now, you pretty poor boy,
　　And you must know what for."

"She is as pure," cried Matthew,
　　"As is the early dew,
　Her only stain it is the pain
　　That around her neck I drew!

"She is as guiltless as the day
　　She sprang forth from her mother.
　The only sin upon her skin
　　Is that she loved another."

They took him off to Bodmin,
　　They pulled the prison bell,
　They sent him smartly up to Heaven
　　And dropped him down to Hell.

All through the granite kingdom
　　And on its travelling airs
　Ask which of these two lovers
　　The most deserves your prayers.

And your steel heart search, Stranger,
　　That you may pause and pray
　For lovers who come not to bed
　　Upon their wedding day,

But lie upon the moorland
　　Where stands the sacred snow
　Above the breathing river,
　　And the salt sea-winds go.

CHARLES CAUSLEY

Cowboys

Panther-footed saunter in the street,
Who spinning six blunt sounds in the mouth's chamber
Tongue-hammer them one by one when they meet.

Evening. Eyes sharpen under somber
Brims, drilling the distance for a spurt of hooves.
These wait only for the Stage to lumber

Between sights, to squander their nine lives
(In a town now dead from the waist up,
For where are the children and the shopping wives?)

They saunter with slack hands, but at the drop
Of a card will conjure guns out of thick air —
Explode every bottle on the bar-top —

Eclipse the lamp with a shooting star —
Struggle under tables, until the one
With the grin knock senseless the one with the scar.

Justice done and seen to be done,
A bullet in front for one in the back,
The honest stranger on the white stallion

cheap
seats at
the
movies

Canters off singing. Shopkeeper and clerk
Lunge to their panther feet in the one-and-nines,
Saunter slack-handed into the dark,

And manfully ride home their bucking trains:
Each wearing, like a medal, his chosen wound
To cancel the reproach of varicose veins.

JON STALLWORTHY

Cowboy Song

I come from Salem County
  Where the silver melons grow,
Where the wheat is sweet as an angel's feet
  And the zithering zephyrs blow.
I walk the blue bone-orchard
  In the apple-blossom snow,
When the teasy bees take their honeyed ease
  And the marmalade moon hangs low.

My Maw sleeps prone on the prairie
  in a boulder eiderdown,
Where the pickled stars in their little jam-jars
  Hang in a hoop to town.
I haven't seen Paw since a Sunday
  In eighteen seventy-three
When he packed his snap in a bitty mess-trap
  And said he'd be home by tea.

Outdoor
meal
lunch box.

Fled is my fancy sister
  All weeping like the willow,
And dead is the brother I loved like no other
  Who once did share my pillow.
I fly the florid water
  Where run the seven geese round,
O the townsfolk talk to see me walk
  Six inches off the ground.

Across the map of midnight
  I trawl the turning sky,
In my green glass the salt fleets pass
  The moon her fire-float by.
The girls go gay in the valley
  Where the boys come down from the farm,
Don't run, my joy, from a poor cowboy,
  I won't do you no harm.

The bread of my twentieth birthday
  I buttered with the sun,
Though I sharpen my eyes with lovers' lies
  I'll never see twenty-one.
Light is my shirt with lilies,
  And lined with lead my hood,
On my face as I pass is a plate of brass,
  And my suit is made of wood.

CHARLES CAUSLEY

The Old Chisholm Trail

Come along, boys, and listen to my tale,
I'll tell you of my troubles on the Old Chisholm Trail.
    Come-a-ki-yi-yippy, come-a-ki-yi-yea. (*twice*)

A ten-dollar horse and a forty-dollar saddle,
And I'm goin' punchin' Texas cattle.
                 (*Chorus*)

It's bacon and beans most every day,
I'd sooner be eatin' prairie hay.
                 (*Chorus*)

Woke up one mornin' on the Old Chisholm Trail,
My rope in my hand and heifer by the tail.
                 (*Chorus*)

Stray in the herd and the boss said kill it,
So we bedded that stray in the bottom of the skillet.
                 (*Chorus*)

It's rainin' and hailin' and blowin' mighty cold,
An' these longhorn sonso'guns are gettin' hard to hold.
(*Chorus*)

I jumped in my saddle and I gave a little yell,
The tail cattle broke and the leaders went to hell.
(*Chorus*)

My feet in the stirrups, my seat in the sky,
Gonna quit herdin' cows in the sweet bye and bye.
(*Chorus*)

I don't give a damn if they never do stop,
I'll ride as long as an eight-day clock.
(*Chorus*)

So I herded and hollered and done very well,
Till the boss said, "Bill, just let 'em go to hell."
(*Chorus*)

Now my old boss is a mighty fine man,
You know there's whiskey wherever he lands.
(*Chorus*)

We rounded 'em up and put 'em on the cars.
The herd   And that was the last of the old Two Bars.
brand.
(*Chorus*)

I went to my boss to draw my roll,
He had me figured out five dollars in the hole.
(*Chorus*)

Me and my boss we had a little chat,
And I slammed him in the face with my ten gallon hat.
(*Chorus*)

I'm goin' to town to spend my money,
Then I'm goin' back South to see my honey.
(*Chorus*)

TRADITIONAL

Florida Road Workers

I'm makin' a road
For the cars
To fly by on.
Makin' a road
Through the palmetto thicket
For light and civilization
To travel on.

Makin' a road
For the rich old white men
To sweep over in their big cars
And leave me standin' here.

Sure,
A road helps all of us!
White folks ride —
And I get to see 'em ride.
I ain't never seen nobody
Ride so fine before.
Hey buddy!
Look at me.
I'm making a road!

LANGSTON HUGHES

Jerónimo's House

My house, my fairy
    palace, is
of perishable
    clapboards with
three rooms in all,
    my gray wasps' nest
of chewed-up paper
    glued with spit.

My home my love-nest
    is endowed
with a veranda
    of wooden lace,
adorned with ferns
    planted in sponges,
and the front room
    with red and green

left-over Christmas
    decorations
looped from the corners
    to the middle
above my little
    center table
of woven wicker
    painted blue,

and four blue chairs
    and an affair
for the smallest baby
    with a tray
with ten big beads.
    Then on the walls
two palm-leaf fans
    and a calendar

and on the table
    one fried fish
spattered with burning
    scarlet sauce,
a little dish
    of hominy grits
and four pink tissue-
    paper roses.

Also I have
    hung on a hook,
an old French horn
    repainted with
aluminum paint.
    I play each year
in the parade
    for José Marti.

At night you'd think
    my house abandoned.
Come closer. You
    can see and hear
the writing-paper
    lines of light
and the voices of
    my radio

singing flamencos
    in between
the lottery numbers.
    When I move
I take these things,
    not much more, from
my shelter from
    the hurricane.

ELIZABETH BISHOP

F for Fig

F for fig,
I for jig, and
N for Knuckley Boney,
I for John the waterman, and
S for Sarah Stoney.

ANONYMOUS

List of Illustrations

(Acknowledgements continued)

Harcourt, Brace & World, Inc.: For "nobody loses all the time" from *Poems 1923-1954* by E. E. Cummings. Copyright 1926 by Horace Liveright; copyright 1954 by E. E. Cummings. For "Phizzog," "Unintentional Paint," "Useless Words," and "Wanting the Impossible," all from *Good Morning, America* by Carl Sandburg. Copyright 1928, 1956 by Carl Sandburg. For extracts from *The People, Yes* by Carl Sandburg. Copyright 1936 by Harcourt, Brace & World, Inc.: copyright 1964 by Carl Sandburg. For "The Pardon" from *Ceremony and Other Poems* by Richard Wilbur. Copyright 1948, 1949, 1950 by Richard Wilbur. All reprinted by permission of Harcourt, Brace & World, Inc.

Harper & Row, Publishers, Inc.: For "Big Bessie Throws Her Son into the Street" by Gwendolyn Brooks. Copyright © 1963 by Gwendolyn Brooks Blakely. For "Life for My Child" from "The Womanhood" by Gwendolyn Brooks. Copyright © 1949 by Gwendolyn Brooks Blakely. Both from *Selected Poems* by Gwendolyn Brooks. For "The Casualty" from *The Hawk in the Rain* by Ted Hughes. Copyright © 1957 by Ted Hughes. For "Travelling Through the Dark" from *Travelling Through the Dark* by William Stafford. Copyright © 1960 by William Stafford. For "Mirror" from *The Carpentered Hen and Other Tame Creatures* by John Updike. Copyright © 1967 by John Updike. Originally appeared in *The New Yorker*, under the title "Reflection." All reprinted by permission of Harper & Row, Publishers, Inc.

Harvard University Press: For "I Took My Power in My Hand." Reprinted by permission of the publishers and the Trustees of Amherst College from Thomas H. Johnson, Editor, *The Poems of Emily Dickinson*, Cambridge, Mass.: The Belknap Press of Harvard University Press, Copyright 1951, 1955, by The President and Fellows of Harvard College.

Holt, Rinehart and Winston, Inc.: For "Choose" from *Chicago Poems* by Carl Sandburg. Copyright 1916 by Holt, Rinehart and Winston, Inc. Copyright 1944 by Carl Sandburg. For "Beyond Words" and "Out, Out—" from *The Complete Poems of Robert Frost*. Copyright © 1923 by Holt, Rinehart and Winston, Inc. Copyright 1936, 1951 by Robert Frost. Copyright 1964 by Lesley Frost Ballantine. All reprinted by permission of Holt, Rinehart and Winston, Inc.

David Higham Associates, Ltd.: For "Cowboy Song" and "Timothy Winters" by Charles Causley. For "The Ballad of Charlotte Dymond" by Charles Causley, from *Modern Folk Ballads*.

Hill and Wang, Inc.: For "First Ice" by Andrei Voznesensky. From *Voznesensky: Selected Poems*, translated by Herbert Marshall. Copyright © 1966 by Herbert Marshall. Reprinted by permission of Hill and Wang, Inc.

Bruce Humphries, Publishers: For "Money" from *Yours for the Asking* (1942) by Richard Armour. By permission of Bruce Humphries, Publishers: Boston, Mass.

M. K. Joseph: For "Girl, Boy, Flower, Bicycle" by M. K. Joseph.

J. B. Lippincott Company: For "The Quarrel" from *Poems for Children* by Eleanor Farjeon. Copyright 1933, 1961 by Eleanor Farjeon. Published by J. B. Lippincott and reprinted by their permission.

Little, Brown and Company: For "I Took My Power in My Hand" from *Complete Poems* by Emily Dickinson.

Liveright Publishing Corporation: For "When You're Away" by Samuel Hoffenstein from *A Treasury of Humorous Verse*.

Longmans, Green & Company: For "Alfred the Great" by Stevie Smith, from *The Frog Prince and Other Poems*.

The Macmillan Company: For "Bags of Meat" (Copyright 1925 by The Macmillan Company, renewed 1953 by Lloyds Bank, Ltd.) and "Heredity" (Copyright 1925 by The Macmillan Company) from *Collected Poems* by Thomas

Index of Titles and Poets